蔡志忠漫画中英文版

菜根谭

THE ROOTS OF WISDOM

人·生·的·滋·味

The Flavor of Life

蔡志忠/著　BRIAN BRUYA(美)/译

现代出版社

Contents

The Roots of Wisdom

Part the First

醲肥辛甘非真味，真味只是淡；神奇卓异非至人，至人只是常。

Know the flavor within the plain
See the wonder within the common

1 Strong, rich, spicy, and sweet are not genuine flavors;

2 Genuine flavor is only plain.

3 People with wondrous and unique skills are not perfect people;

4 The most perfect people are only common.

Exciting and novel things don't last very long. Only plain and common things endure over time. Anything that is too contrived has lost its original face. Only the natural is genuine.

1

Heaven and earth seem serene and still, though the seasons rest not for an instant;

The sun and moon course along, though their brightness has always been constant.

2

So a gentleman in leisure should keep urgent thoughts...

And a leisurely humor when busy.

We should emulate nature, changing amid the constant, constant amid the changes. In leisure, the mind shouldn't be too relaxed, and in urgency, we shouldn't be too tense.

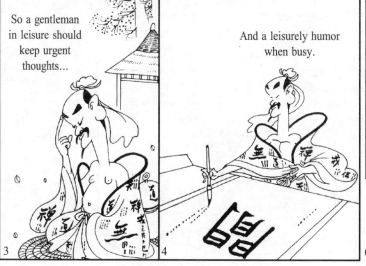

3

4

人生的滋味——菜根谭

处要有悠闲的趣味。

天地寂然不动，而气机无息稍停；日月尽夜奔驰，而贞明万古不易。故君子闲时要有吃紧的心思，忙

3

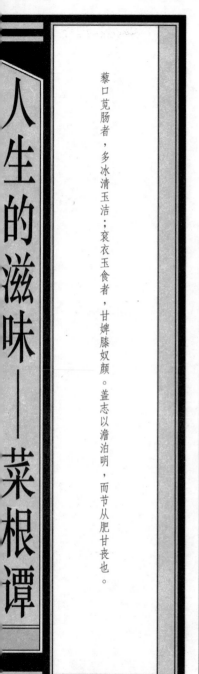

藜口苋肠者，多冰清玉洁；衮衣玉食者，甘婢膝奴颜。盖志以澹泊明，而节从肥甘丧也。

In plainness is ambition realized In richness is integrity compromised

1 One with pigweed in the mouth and amaranth in the gut,

2 Is as pure as jade, as clear as ice.

3 One who wears dragon robes and eats jade,

4 Will kneel like a maid-servant and grin like a slave...

5 Because aspirations are realized through plain simplicity,

6 While integrity is compromised by the rich and sweet.

People who don't seek favors from others are naturally upright. Someone who prefers to eat coarse food, like pigweed and amaranth, isn't moved by temptation

Opened wide before you Enduring kindness after

1 Open wide the fields before you,

2 And others will have no grumblings against you.

His conduct is impeccable!

I can't complain.

What a guy!

3 Leave kindness that endures behind you,

4 And others will remember you forever.

If you open up your heart to others in generosity and caring, no one will be dissatisfied with you. If you give of yourself for the benefit of others, you will naturally be remembered.

面前的田地要放得宽，使人无不平之叹；身后的恩泽要流得久，使人有不匮之思。

人生的滋味──菜根谭

5

人生的滋味——菜根谭

径路窄处，留一步与人行；滋味浓的，减三分让人尝。此是涉世一极安乐法。

On a path,
yield a step
In tasting,
share a bite

1 Where the path is narrow, step aside for others to pass.

2 Thank You.

You go ahead.

3 When the flavor is rich, subtract a few parts for others to taste.

4 This is a very comfortable way of handling affairs.

"In the affairs of the world, yield a few parts, for heaven is vast and the earth broad; in the field of the mind, cultivate a bit, that your descendants may reap from the seeds you sow." How much you yield to others determines how well others treat you.

Chivalry in making friends
Purity in living life

1

Making friends demands a little chivalry.

交友須帶三分俠氣，做人要存一點素心。

人生的滋味——菜根谭

2

Living life requires some naivet.

Good friends are supportive of each other, sharing the good times and working together through the hard times. In conducting ourselves, we should maintain a heart of natural simplicity, sincerity, and child-like naivet.

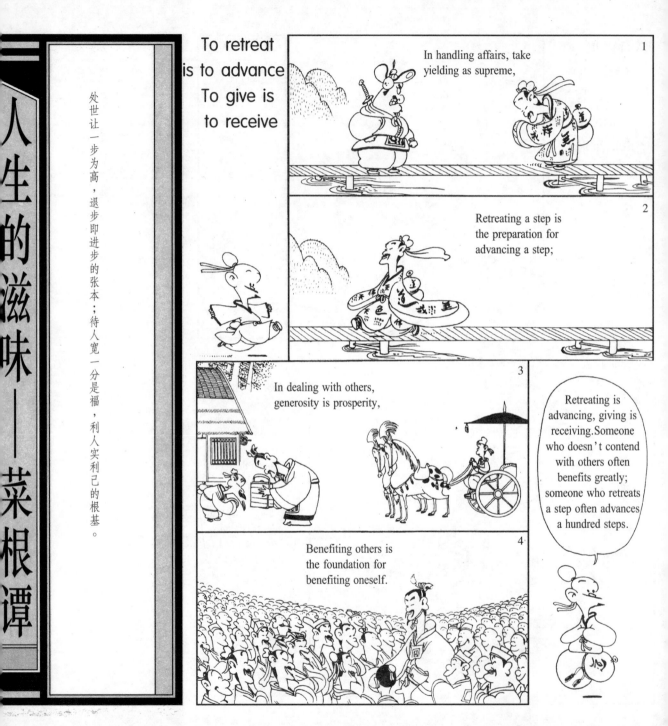

人生的滋味——菜根谭

处世让一步为高，退步即进步的张本；待人宽一分是福，利人实利己的根基。

To retreat is to advance To give is to receive

1 In handling affairs, take yielding as supreme,

2 Retreating a step is the preparation for advancing a step;

3 In dealing with others, generosity is prosperity,

4 Benefiting others is the foundation for benefiting oneself.

Retreating is advancing, giving is receiving. Someone who doesn't contend with others often benefits greatly; someone who retreats a step often advances a hundred steps.

Arrogance negates achievement Repentance annuls misdeeds

1

The most distinguished deeds in the world...

2

Cannot bear up under the one word "arrogance".

3

The most ignominious crimes under the sun...

4

Cannot bear up under the one word "repentance".

Even if you have accomplished great things, pride and arrogance will bring your eventual downfall. And even if you have done horrible things, sincere repentance can make up for it.

人生的滋味——菜根谭

盖世功劳，当不得一个矜字；弥天罪过，当不得一个悔字。

好动者，云电风灯；嗜寂者，死灰槁木。须定云止水中，有鸢飞鱼跃气象，才是有道的心体。

人生的滋味——菜根谭

Movement and stillness in harmony are the Dao's genuine body

1

An excessively active person is like lightning in the clouds, a flame in the wind.

2

An overly serene person is like dead ash, a dried up branch.

3

One must instead be like a soaring kite among still clouds,

4

A leaping fish in placid water...

5

In order to possess the mind and body of the Dao.

Active

Tranquil

The only way to maintain true delight is to be tranquil in action and active in tranquillity.

居轩冕之中，不可无山林的气味；处林泉之下，须要怀廊庙的经纪。

人生的滋味——菜根谭

人生的滋味——菜根譚

忧勤是美德，太苦则无以适性怡情；澹泊是高风，太枯则无以济人利物。

Do not let industry become drudgery
Do not treat others with indifference

1

Industry is a fair virtue,

2

But sheer drudgery lends no joy to the spirit;

3

Simplicity is of high merit,

4

But stark indifference helps no one and nothing.

If in conducting all affairs we can maintain a balanced and unbiased attitude, our happiness and joy will be never-ending.

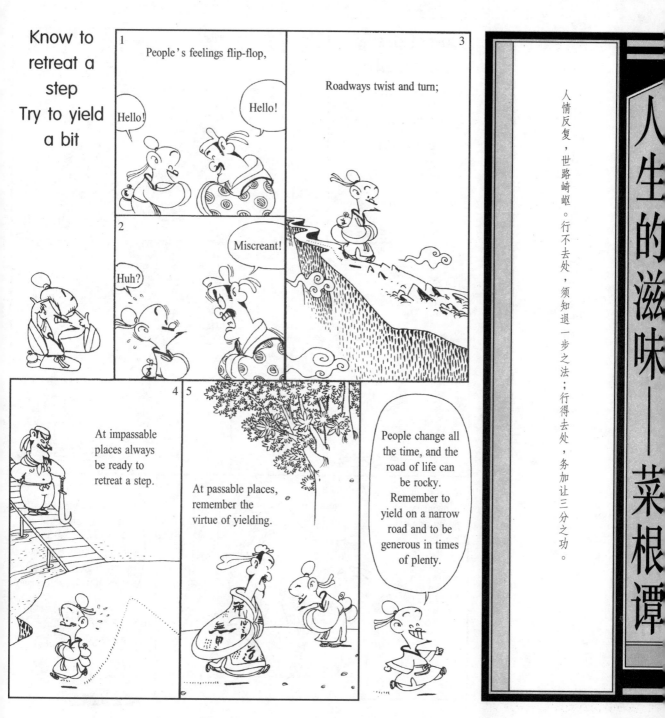

人生的滋味——菜根谭

待小人，不难于严，而难于不恶；待君子，不难于恭，而难于有礼。

Do not despise the underling
Treat the gentleman with propriety

It is not difficult to be strict with an underling; what is difficult is not despising him.

1

You clumsy fool! You're lazy, and you're stupid!

I'm afraid he didn't forgive me...

2

It is not difficult to respect a gentleman;

3

What is difficult is maintaining propriety around him.

Ha ha ha. Bottom's up, good buddy!

clink!

4

Sometimes it is difficult for us to treat a person of lower station with appropriate compassion and to treat an admirable person with appropriate dignity.

Transcending heaven and earth Entering among fame and fortune

1 Though another is wealthy, still I am benevolent;

Rich

Benevolent

2 Though another is titled, still I am righteous;

Titled

Righteous

3 For a gentleman is not ensnared by illusions of nobility;

4 A focused person transcends fate; a concentrated will stirs one's energy;

5 For a gentleman is not restrained by the mold of the creator.

Rather than being fettered by the expectations that are thrust upon us and giving in to desires that surround us, we should transcend our environment and live with dignity and integrity.

陶铸。

彼富我仁，彼爵我义，君子固不为君相所牢笼；人定胜天，志一动气，君子亦不受造物之

人生的滋味——菜根谭

人生的滋味——菜根谭

学者要收拾精神，并归一路。如修德而留意于事功名誉，必无实诣；读书而寄兴于吟咏风雅，定不深心。

Cultivating virtue takes forgetting fame Acquiring knowledge requires a mind of depth

1
A student must gather his energies and concentrate on one path.

2
If while cultivating virtue he daydreams about achievement and fame, surely there will be no fruition.

3
Springtime has the hundred flowers, autumn has the moon, Summer has a cooling breeze, and winter has the snow...

If while studying he merely recites the elegant lines...

4
Surely he will never have a mind of depth.

The purpose of study is in cultivating virtue.If you emphasize only the advancement of knowledge or the beauty of literature, you've missed the significance of studying. Self-cultivation and study go hand in hand, and both require concentration and perseverance.

The ways of truth and deceit reside in a single thought

1

Everyone possesses great mercy, and there is no difference between a saint or butcher.

西得故菩提薩埵依般若波羅蜜多故心無
里礙無罣礙故無有恐怖遠離一切顛倒夢
想究竟涅槃三世諸佛依般若波羅蜜多
得阿耨多羅三藐三菩提故知般若波羅蜜
多是大神咒是大明咒是無上咒是無等等
咒能除一切苦真實不虛故說般若波羅蜜
多咒即說咒曰

3

It's just that our desires and passions often blind us,

All places have a touch of charm, and there is no disparity between a golden chamber and a thatched hut.

2

4

And at the point of departure, the difference of an inch can mean a thousand miles.

"Everyone has a sense of right and wrong." People are originally good but can be trapped by passions and desires. Isn't this as tragic as a bright-eyed person who suddenly goes blind?

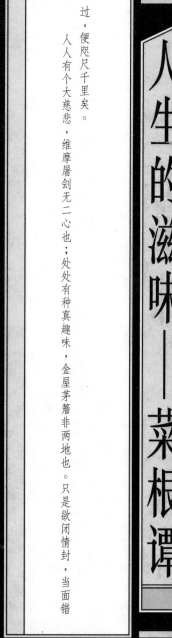

An evil person's learning Serves to abet evil

1 One's heart must be pure before studying the ancients,

2 Otherwise, in learning good actions, one might usurp them for selfish ends,

Well said! I can use this method myself.

3 Or in learning good speech, one might use it to conceal one's shortcomings;

See, this ancient scholar said the same thing I did!

4 This is like giving weapons to the enemy or grain to bandits.

These are for you!

hee hee

If put to good use, our studies can aid in cultivating the self and governing the country. But if our hearts are sullied, learning can also be used for all sorts of unmentionable things.

心地干净，方可读书学古。不然，见一善行窃以济私，闻一善言假以覆短，是又藉寇兵而赍盗粮矣。

人生的滋味——菜根谭

Long for sageliness in learning, practice what you preach. Care for the people when in office, cultivate virtue in your career.

1

If you do not meet the sages and worthies while studying,

2

You are like a printing plate engraver.

3

If you do not care for the people while serving in office, you are like a bandit in court robes.

Namah Amitabha
Namah Amitabha
Namah Amitabha
Namah Amitabha
tock tock tock
tock

4

To not practice what you preach is lip-service Zen.

5

To not plant seeds of virtue in establishing your career is to have blossoms fade in front of you.

In all affairs, there are the genuine and the false. The goal of studying is to learn the principles, not to get the best grade. A virtuous career is the foundation on which accomplishment is built.

人生的滋味——菜根谭

欹器以满覆，扑满以空全。故君子宁居无不居有，宁处缺不处完。

Do not envy eminence
Do not dread hunger

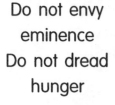

人知名位为乐，不知无名无位之乐为最真；人知饥寒为忧，不知不饥不寒之忧为更甚。

1

People know that fame and status are joyful things,

2

But they don't realize that having neither fame nor status is the most genuine joy.

3

People know that being hungry and cold are dreadful things,

4

But they don't realize that never being hungry or cold can be even more dreadful.

There's no such thing as absolute good or bad. Everything has its advantages and disadvantages, it all depends on how you look at it!

23

人生的滋味——菜根谭

为恶而畏人知，恶中犹有善路；为善而急人知，善处即是恶根。

羞，一生无病是吾忧。」真确论也。

泛驾之马可就驰驱，跃冶之金终归型范。只一优游不振，便终身无个进步。白沙云：「为人多病未足

A country
prospers
through worry
and toil
The self is lost
through idle
leisure

1

A violent horse can still be made to run;

2

Metal that leaps out of the smelt can still be returned to the mold.

3

Play without effort means a life without progress.

Hey, you guys, don't just sit there and dodge the world.

4

Chen Xianzhang once said:

To have many faults is not worth feeling ashamed about. What I worry about is going through life without having any faults at all.

5

How true!

Don't be afraid of having faults. Be afraid instead of not making the effort to correct your faults.

人生的滋味——菜根谭

所以度越一世。

人只一念贪私，便销刚为柔，塞智为昏，变恩为惨，染洁为污，坏了一生人品。故古人以不贪为宝，

A single thought of selfish greed A thousand pains without return

A moment's selfish greed...

1

Turns strength into weakness,

2

I know I shouldn't take what's not mine, but...

Intelligence into confusion,

3

There's so much, it won't matter if I take a little...

Kindness into cruelty,

4

Can't stop once you've started, might as well take it all!

And purity into pollution,

5

Destroying one's character for life.

6

Don't move!

The ancients took uncovetousness as the most precious thing of all and so were able to transcend material desires for a lifetime.

7

When greed begins, the conscience is destroyed, we lose our powers of discrimination, and intelligence turns into confusion and ignorance.

If the master of the mind is on alert
The bandits six shall show no trace

1. What the eyes and ears see and hear become our outer bandits;

ears / eyes

2. Passion, desire, and conscious thought become our inner bandits.

Ha haha ha ha

Ha haha ha ha

3. But as long as the head of the household stays alert,

Stay pure and self-possessed

4. And sits with authority in the central hall,

5. The bandits will transform into members of the family.

ears / eyes / body / thoughts / nose / mouth / tongue

Internal and external temptations can perplex us and mislead us. So we must always be alert and preserve the clarity of the original mind.

耳目见闻为外贼，情欲意识为内贼。只是主人翁惺惺不昧，独坐中堂，贼便化为家人矣。

图未就之功，不如保已成之业；悔既往之失，不如防将来之非。

Pushing the present enterprise Planning for future success

1 2

Planning feats one is not yet capable of...

Is not so good as maintaining an already successful enterprise.

3

Regretting past losses,

4

Is not so good as preventing future mistakes.

Stay practical and work outward from a stable foundation. If you fail, learn from your mistake without dwelling on it.

Not caught up in material things
Not keeping the sounds and shadows

The wind sweeps through bamboo. The wind goes, and the bamboo keeps no sound.

2

A wild goose crosses a wintry lake,

The goose leaves, and the lake holds no shadow.

3

So when something happens, a gentleman reacts,

4

whap!

5

And when it's over, his mind returns to emptiness.

We often make ourselves suffer by fretting over what's to come and regretting what we've done.

风来疏竹，风过而竹不留声；雁渡寒潭，雁去而潭不留影；故君子之事来而心始现，事去而心随空。

人生的滋味—菜根谭

人生的滋味——菜根谭

真机。

静中静非真静，动处静得来，才是性天之真境；乐处乐非真乐，苦中乐得来，才是心体之

Tranquillity amid tumult is genuine tranquillity Pleasure amid hardship is genuine pleasure

1 To find tranquillity amid tranquillity is not genuine tranquillity;

2 Only tranquillity found in a tumultuous place is the spiritual realm of the genuine.

To find delight in a delightful place is not genuine delight;

3

4 Only delight found amid hardship is the physical ground of the genuine.

Our attitude often changes with our surroundings, but if we can transcend our surroundings, we can attain spiritual and physical genuineness.

Strive to cultivate achievement and virtue
Do not covet power and status

1. If a commoner is willing to cultivate virtue and extend kindness,

2. Then he is an untitled noble.

You're a savior!

3. If a noble merely plots for power and curries favor,

Oh, his majesty is so intelligent, so great!

4. Then he is a titled beggar.

You're a good sycophant. Here's a new title for you.

Oh, I thank His Majesty. Thank you! Thank you!

A person's value is determined not by his position but by his virtue. What's the difference between a superior who goes around groveling to everyone in order to gain more power and a beggar on the street?

平民肯种德施惠，便是无位的公相；士夫徒贪权市宠，竟成有爵的乞人。

人生的滋味——菜根谭

31

文章做到极处，无有他奇，只是恰好；人品做到极处，无有他异，只是本然。

A perfect essay takes no unusual skill A perfect character is simply natural

There is nothing unusual about a perfect essay, it is simply done just right!

Wow, it's just right. Not one word too many or one word too few.

Excellent

Wonderful!

There is nothing unique about perfect character, it is simply natural.

His virtue is absolutely flawless.

Whatever the situation, just act naturally instead of trying to force things. Boasting and pretending do not yield good results.

人生的滋味——菜根谭

小处不渗漏，暗处不欺隐，末路不怠荒，才是个真正英雄。

千金难结一时之欢，一饭竟致终身之感。盖爱重反为仇，薄极翻成喜也。

Love too heavy turns to hate
A meager jot can turn to joy

1

A small gift for you.

Just set it right there.

A thousand gold pieces rarely bring a moment's favor,

2

Yet a single meal can bring a lifetime of gratefulness;

Take this bowl of rice...

Thank you! Thank you!

3

Because love too heavy turns to hate,

You ungrateful wretch!

You underhanded dirty dog.

4

While a meager jot can turn to joy.

I remember that time years ago when you gave me a bowl of rice to relieve my hunger.

Love should not be built on material things.Instead, care should be given at the proper times.What's more practical adding ornament to brocade or giving fuel on a snowy day?

Do not open up to the devious
Do not say much to the arrogant

Do not open up to the inscrutable and reserved;

Careful what you say to the impassioned and boastful.

A person who is cold and silent is often cunning and difficult to gauge, so don't get too close. A person who is short-tempered and arrogant is usually stubborn and close-minded, so be careful what you say.

遇沉沉不语之士，且莫输心；见悻悻自好之人，应须防口。

人生的滋味——菜根谭

人生的滋味——菜根谭

觉人之诈，不形于言，受人之侮，不动于色，此中有无穷意味，亦有无穷受用。

Forbear much
Reveal little

People are microcosms of the universe
The universe is the parent of people

1 My body is a small universe,

2 So that my emotions lead not to transgressions...

3 And my predilections remain principled; this is its harmonizing skill.

The universe is a great parent so that people have no complaints and things suffer no blight; this is its congenial atmosphere.

4 People are naturally endowed with emotions and personal biases, but we also possess the skill to balance these and conduct ourselves in a principled manner.

人生的滋味——菜根谭

疹，亦是敦睦的气象。

吾身一小天地也，使喜怒不愆，好恶有则，便是燮理的功夫；天地一大父母也，使民无怨咨，物无氛疹

人生的滋味——菜根谭

德者才之主，才者德之奴。有才无德，如家无主而奴用事矣，几何不魍魎猖狂？

Virtue should guide talent Without talent shirking virtue

1

Virtue is the master of ability. Ability is the servant of virtue.

Virtue

Talent

2

Talent without virtue is like a household without a head and the servants handling all the affairs.

Yes, master

Do this! Do that!

Virtue

Talent

Go forward, and keep walking.

Yes, master.

Is this not a monster out of control?

An talented person without virtue tends to be despotic and defiant of authority, so he ends up being harmful rather than beneficial to society!

Talent

Virtue

virtue

3

43

人生的滋味——菜根谭

饥则附，饱则飏，燠则趋，寒则弃，人情通患也。

To flock to power and influence is common to human nature

To flock to others when hungry...

And fly away when fed,

To cling to someone who is hot..

And turn away when he is cold.

This is an ailment across human nature!

It is so common for us to treat wealthy and powerful people differently from poor and weak people. Indeed, it seems to be an illness that everyone has!

念回光，炯然返照，始知耳目口鼻皆桎梏，而情欲嗜好悉机械矣。

一灯萤然，万籁无声，此吾人初入宴寂时也；晓梦初醒，群动未起，此吾人初出混沌处也。乘此而一

When the human heart is unresolved The moral mind is indistinct

1 In the soft glow of a lamp, when all noises cease—

2 This is when we begin to go into repose.

3 Coming out of dreams at dawn, before the hosts begin to stir this is when we begin to leave a groggy state.

4 If at these times we can take a moment for introspection, we'll come to realize that our ears, eyes, nose, and mouth, are but shackles,

eyes
ears
nose
mouth

5 And that our passions, desires, and infatuations are mechanisms of downfall.

Just before going to sleep and just after waking up are when the world is quiet and the mind is clear. If we can take advantage of this time for introspection, we will reap great benefits.

而乐自存。

水不波则自定，鉴不翳则自明。故心无可清，去其混之者，而清自现；乐不必寻，去其苦之者，

1 When the clouds are gone, the moon appears When the dust is cleared, the mirror shines

Water undisturbed is naturally calm;

2 A mirror uncovered is naturally bright.

3 So the mind cannot be made clear; just eliminate delusion, and the mind will naturally be clear.

4 Happiness need not be sought after;

5 just eliminate suffering, and happiness will naturally exist.

The mind is naturally clear, but it is often obscured by delusions and distractions. If we can just eliminate these, the clarity of the original mind will naturally shine through.

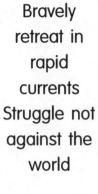

Bravely retreat in rapid currents Struggle not against the world

人生的滋味——菜根谭

1

In retiring, retire at a time of highest achievement;

2

In residing, reside in a place of solitary retreat.

Only by withdrawing can you avoid the aftermath that achievement brings. You won't incur the displeasure of others if you are humble and refrain from contending for glory and fame with them.

人生的滋味——菜根谭

人嘉言懿行。

交市人不如友山翁，谒朱门不如亲白屋；听街谈巷语，不如闻樵歌牧咏；谈今人失德过举，不如述古

Better to have plain simplicity than elaborate embellishment
Better to recount the ancients than discuss the moderns

1 Better to befriend a mountain recluse than interact with a city man;

2 Better to chat with a commoner than meet with a magnate.

3 Better to hear the songs of woodcutters and shepherd boys than listen to the gossip of streets and alleyways;

4 Better to recount the great words and actions of the ancients than discuss the transgressions and wrongdoing of the moderns.

Mountain recluses seek tranquillity, commoners are mild, shepherd boys' songs are heartwarming, and recounting the ancients can inspire us.

Cultivating virtue within yourself is the foundation of successful endeavor

德者事業之基，未有基不固而棟宇堅久者。

人生的滋味——菜根譚

1

Virtue is the foundation of any endeavor;

virtue

2

There has never been a lasting and stable structure without a firm foundation.

Any endeavor must be established on a strong foundation, otherwise it just won't last; and the strongest foundation of all is virtue.

人生的滋味——菜根谭

心者后裔之根，未有根不植而枝叶荣茂者。

With a good heart, children and grandchildren prosper
With strong roots, leaves and branches flourish

1

A good heart is the rootstock for one's descendants;

2

There has never been a plant that flourished without healthy roots.

A good heart allows for decency and kindness toward others, which will be repaid over and over to one's children and grandchildren.

人生的滋味——菜根譚

自昧所有，一箴自夸所有，可为学问切戒。

前人云：「抛却自家无尽藏，沿门持钵效贫儿。」又云：「暴富贫儿休说梦，谁家灶里火无烟。一箴

Do not be quick to belittle yourself
Do not boast or act arrogantly

1. Someone once said:
Abandoning one's very own inexhaustible treasure, door to door with bowl in hand, just like the needy ones.

2. It is also said:
Oh, needy one, with newfound riches, do not speak of dreams, for in whose hearth that sits at home is fire without the smoke?

3. The first verse advises us not to overlook what we possess, And the second to not boast of what we possess.

4. They are both good precepts for the student.

Everything under the sun is unique and possesses it's own worth. Don't compare yourself with others, don't belittle your own worth, and don't think too highly of yourself.

53

人生的滋味——菜根谭

道是一重公众物事，当随人而接引。学是一个寻常家饭，当随事而警惕。

The Dao is a public thing Learning is a home-cooked meal

1

The Dao is a public thing,

2

And we should approach it individually.

3

Learning is a home-cooked meal,

I learn from people's good points and bad points.

4

Learning is as simple as a home-cooked meal and is something that everyone can pursue. As long as we are open-minded, there is something to learn in every situation.

And we should always be alert.

Be severe with yourself and lenient toward others

Pardon the transgressions [1] of others,

I'll forgive you this time, and I hope you'll do better next time.

I'll try.

2

But not your own.

Strict with oneself Lenient toward others

3

You can do it, you can do it...

Forbear in your own hardships,

4

But not in others'.

We should always be strict with ourselves and lenient towards others. When you have difficulties, strive to work through them; and when others have difficulties, lend a helping hand.

人之过误宜恕，而在己则不可恕；己之困辱宜忍，而在人则不可忍。

人生的滋味——菜根谭

人生的滋味——菜根谭

侮我，我胡为怒。

我贵而人奉之，奉此峨冠大带也；我贱而人侮之，侮此布衣草履也。然则原非奉我，我胡为喜；原非

**People's feelings are warm and cold
The world's attitude is hot and cool**

1 When I have a high status, people show respect, but what they respect are my high hat and broad belt.

2 When I am destitute, people insult me,

3 But what they insult are my coarse clothes and straw sandals.

4 So since it is not me they respect, why should I feel happy? And since it is not me they insult, why should I feel angry?

Reputation, wealth, and status are all external things, so there is no reason to be happy when you get them or sad when you lose them. Superficial things cannot bring genuine happiness.

A mind of compassion
A motive for life

1 "To leave some food for the sake of the mice."

2 "To not light a candle on behalf of the moths."

3 Ancient people had these kinds of ideas, and they are ideas to live by.

4 Without them, we might as well be made of clay and wood.

Compassion is in the original nature of all sentient beings. All good karma arises from compassion, and if we don't live by it, we are nothing more than walking corpses.

「为鼠常留饭，怜蛾不点灯」，古人此等念头，是吾人一点生生之机。无此，便所谓土木形骸而已。

人生的滋味——菜根谭

人生的滋味——菜根譚

居官有二語，曰：「唯公則生明，唯廉則生威。」居家有二語，曰：「唯恕則情平，唯儉則用足。」

In
prosperity,
understand
poverty
In stability,
think about
peril

When living in prosperity, understand the suffering of poverty.

If we go on squandering money like this, we'll all be destitute soon...

1

If I keep goofing off like this, I'll end up an old drunk...

2

When young and strong, think about the bitterness of being old.

Without distant worries, trouble will be near at hand.

处富贵之地，要知贫贱的痛痒；当少壮之时，须念衰老的辛酸。

59

休与小人仇仇，小人自有对头；休向君子谄媚，君子原无私惠。

Do not antagonize the petty one Do not flatter the gentleman

1 Keep from becoming a petty person's enemy;

2 A petty person naturally has his adversary.

3 Keep from trying to curry a gentleman's favor;

4 A gentleman does not hold to personal favors.

Getting mixed up with a petty person will only increase your troubles. Ingratiating yourself with a gentleman will only bring disdain.

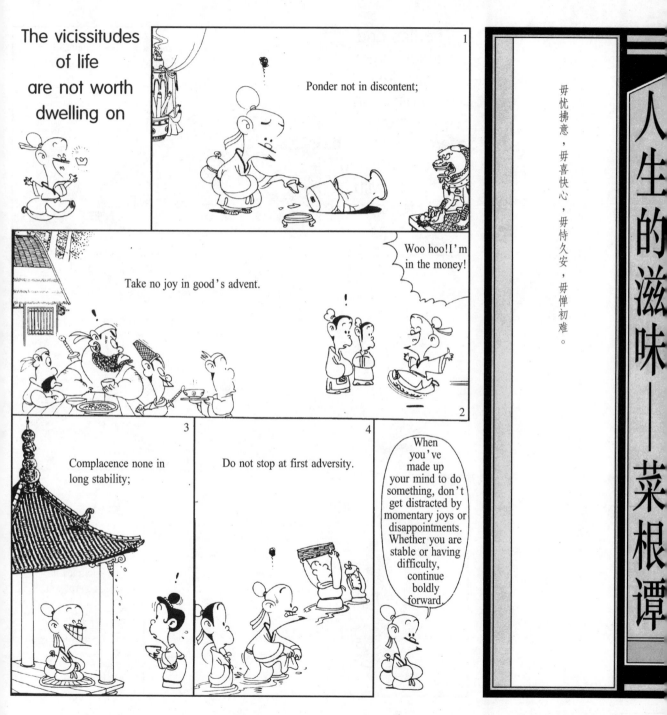

人生的滋味——菜根谭

饮宴之乐多，不是个好人家；声华之习胜，不是个好士子；名位之念重，不是个好臣士。

Parties and pleasure, music and lust, reputation and status

Several things to be approached with temperance

1 A man who takes too much pleasure in drink and banquets is not a man of the family.

2 A man who is too accustomed to music and splendor is not a man of learning.

3 A man who thinks too much about reputation and status is not a man of the people.

It's all right to occasionally indulge in one's desires, but don't let pleasure control you.

Observe
others
coolly
Conduct
affairs
intelligently

Observe with a
cool eye;

Listen with a cool ear;

Feel with cool emotions;

Contemplate with
a cool mind.

Our emotions are
often conflicting,
but if we look at
things from all sides,
coolly evaluate others,
and make rational
decisions, mistakes
won't be easily
made.

冷眼观人；冷耳听语；冷情当感；冷心思理。

人生的滋味——菜根谭

63

人生的滋味——菜根谭

性躁心粗者，一事无成；心和气平者，百福自集。

A frenzied nature injures the world
Peace and harmony invite blessings

1 A person of frenzied nature and rash thoughts shall never accomplish anything;

2 I've failed again...

3 A person of mild thoughts and peaceful temperament...

4 Shall accumulate good fortune.

Someone who is cautious and thorough in everything will naturally succeed, while someone who carelessly plunges into any old thing will usually fail.

人生的滋味——菜根谭

用人不宜刻，刻则思效者去；交友不宜滥，滥则贡谀者来。

Do not make blithe promises or lose your temper
Do not meddle in others' affairs or fail to finish

1 Do not make blithe promises on account of being joyful.

Don't worry! You can count on me!

Thank you!

2 Do not lose your temper due to inebriation.

3 Do not meddle in other people's affairs on account of indignation.

4 Do not fail to finish due to your own exhaustion.

When joyful, drunk, indignant, or tired, give yourself some room to think. Don't do something rash that you'll regret later.

不可乘喜而轻诺，不可因醉而生嗔，不可乘快而多事，不可因倦而鲜终。

人生的滋味——菜根谭

67

人生的滋味——菜根谭

口乃心之门，守口不密，泄尽真机；意乃心之足，防意不严，走尽邪蹊。

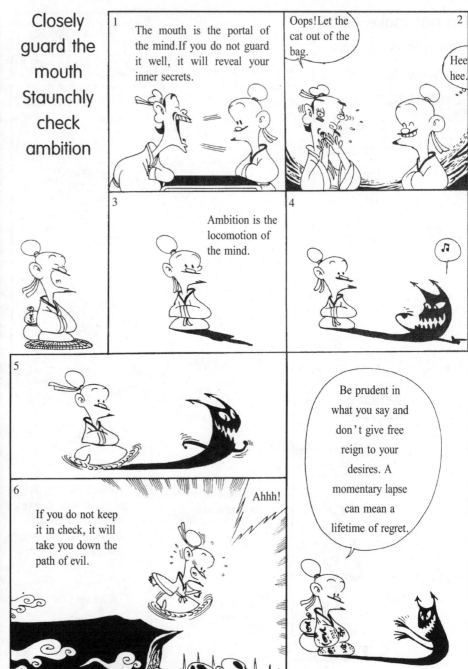

Closely guard the mouth Staunchly check ambition

1 The mouth is the portal of the mind. If you do not guard it well, it will reveal your inner secrets.

2 Oops! Let the cat out of the bag.

Hee hee.

3 Ambition is the locomotion of the mind.

5

6 If you do not keep it in check, it will take you down the path of evil.

Ahhh!

Be prudent in what you say and don't give free reign to your desires. A momentary lapse can mean a lifetime of regret.

Neither troubled in hardship Nor fearful of authority

1

A gentleman is not apprehensive in the midst of trouble;

2

It is during feasts and merrymaking that he worries.

3

He does not fear in the face of the powerful and brutal;

4

It is toward the man without a family that he feels alarmed.

A gentleman is courageous and steadfast. He is not concerned with other people's opinions of him, he does not immerse himself in carnal pleasures, and he helps the needy.

君子处患难而不忧，当宴游而惕虑；遇权豪而不惧，对茕独而惊心。

人生的滋味——菜根谭

The Roots of Wisdom

Part the Second

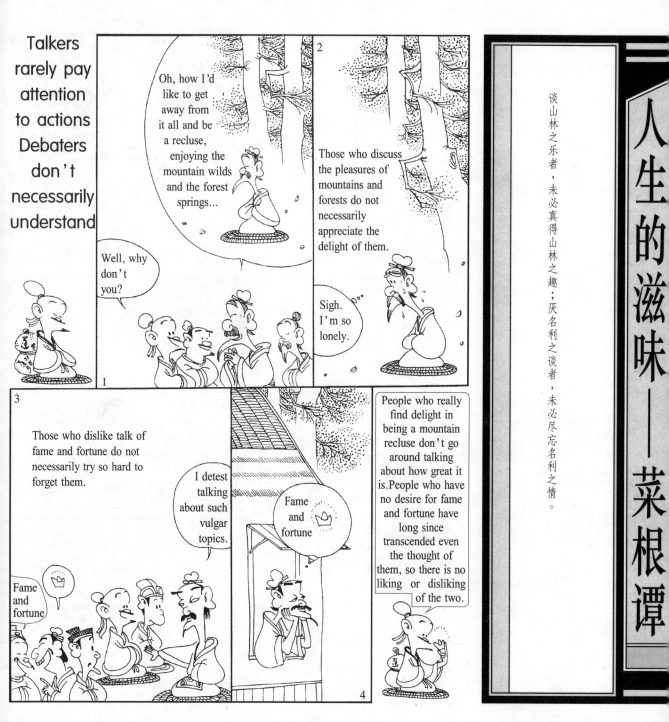

人生的滋味——菜根谭

得趣不在多，盆池拳石间，烟霞俱足；会景不在远，蓬窗竹屋下，风月自赊。

Taking joy in nature's delights Stunning views are never far

Delight lies not in quantity;

1

2

Among a tiny pool and small rocks a landscape is complete.

A single blossom is a world. A single leaf is the Buddha.

3

4

Vistas lie not in distant places;

Within a humble window and bamboo hut a vantage is replete.

5

"In practicing Zen, what need for hills and streams? Extinguish the mind, and fire becomes cool." If we understand how to enjoy life, we can find the truth in any place.

The mind quiet, original substance appears
The water clear, the moon's reflection shines

Hearing the toll of a bell on a quiet night, you wake from a dream within a dream.

bong bong

Looking at the moon's reflection on a clear lake, you see the self outside the self.

Hearing the sudden toll of a bell on a hushed night we feel an air of peace and become aware of everything around us. Just then, all the delusions of daily life become clear.

听静夜之钟声，唤醒梦中之梦；观澄潭之月影，窥见身外之身。

人生的滋味——菜根谭

人生的滋味——菜根谭

人解读有字书，不解读无字书。知弹有弦琴，不知弹无弦琴。以迹用，不以神用，何以得琴书之趣。

Better to see the interior than know the exterior
The spirit employed always beats the form employed

1

2 People try to understand books with words,

But not the wordless books.

For the good student, everything is a book. Landscapes are books; amusements are books, nature's details are books.

3 People try to appreciate zithers with strings,

4 But not the stringless zithers.

There is music everywhere if you just have the mind to hear it.

If we employ the form but not the spirit, how will we ever know the delight of books and zithers?

5 If you see and hear with the mind, you'll discover that everywhere there are wordless books and stringless zithers.

The heart free of desire quiets heaven and earth
A home with books and music becomes a magic kingdom

1 If the heart is free of material desires,

2 It is an autumn sky, a vast sea.

3 If the home has music and books,

4 It is a rocky hideaway, a magic kingdom.

If you free yourself of material desires, a square inch can be as vast as the sea and the sky. If you maintain a simple lifestyle, subtle joys can be found in everything around you.

心无物欲，即是秋空霁海；坐有琴书，便成石室丹丘。

人生的滋味——菜根谭

77

80

人生的滋味—菜根谭

松涧边，携杖独行，立处云生破衲。竹窗下，枕书高卧，觉时月侵寒毡。

I make friends with the leisurely clouds and take the scenery as my home

1 With cane in hand, he walks alone along a pine-covered valley;

And where he stands, clouds gather to his tattered clothes.

2 Beneath a bamboo window, he sleeps deeply with books for a pillow;

3 And when he wakes, the moon penetrates his chilly blanket.

Little is needed to enjoy the subtle charm of nature. Anyone can experience it.

Recluses have no honor or disgrace Morality knows neither hot nor cold

The reclusive one is intelligent Reducing tasks brings peace

Fleeing fame is more delightful than promoting it;

There is really nothing I can't do well.

Could you copy this in your fine calligraphy please?

Sure.

I have one as well. Would you mind?

No, no, not at all.

Reducing tasks is more relaxing than being skilled at tasks.

Not only am I good, but I'm fast. Be done in just a moment.

"Great wisdom resembles foolishness; great skill resembles crudeness." A person with truly great talent often keeps it hidden, thus saving himself troubles.

To transcend splendor and solitude
To be at comfort anywhere

1

A lover of solitude sees the wonder in white clouds and curious rocks.

2

A seeker of splendor forgets his cares in clear singing and clever dancing.

3

Only the self-sufficient man is without splendor or solitude, so wherever he goes is a comfortable patch of the sky.

This is nice.

This isn't bad, either.

Being carefree and at ease means not letting circumstance influence you. If you are happy inside, you will be happy anywhere.

人生的滋味——菜根谭

适之天。

嗜寂者，观白云幽石而通玄；趋荣者，见清歌妙舞而忘倦。唯自得之士，无喧寂，无荣枯，无往非自

人生的滋味——菜根谭

孤云出岫，去留一无所系；朗镜悬空，静躁两不相干。

Enlightened ones have no attachments Quiet and calm make no difference

Lonely cloud emerging from cliffs, no attachment to going or staying;

1

Bright mirror hanging in space, clamor and quiet make no difference.

Ha ha ha ha ha

Ha ha ha ha ha

Ha ha ha ha ha

Ha ha ha ha ha

Inner desires tend to follow the external world, but if you don't let yourself get attached to the external world, you will be free to come and go as you please.

2

Understanding is found in simplicity Enlightenment isn't far away

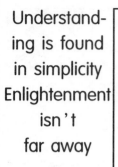

1

In Zen, it is said:

When hungry come and eat some food, when tired come and sleep.

2

In poetry, it is said:

Intricate scenes before the eyes are set in common tongue.

3 The highest profundity is hidden in the most mundane;

4 The utmost difficulty should be approached from utmost simplicity.

The Dao is found in daily life. Grasp the things near at hand and experience their inherent principles. The insights thus gained are the most genuine kind of learning.

5 The one of ambition goes seeking far away;

Dao

6 The one of no-mind, finds it right nearby.

87

人生的滋味——菜根谭

水流而境无声，得处喧见寂之趣；山高而云不碍，悟出有入无之机。

Holding on means a sea of suffering Letting go means a land of paradise

1 Mountains and forests are wonderful places, but with attachment, they become a market or court;

2 Calligraphy and painting are elegant tasks, but with infatuation, they become products for sale.

3 So to an unpolluted mind, the world of desire is a city of angels;

4 But to a mind with attachments, the realm of pleasures becomes a sea of suffering.

To reach the pure land, purify your mind. When the mind is pure, the Buddha-realm is pure. If you can maintain a pure mind, everywhere you go will be a paradise.

人生的滋味——菜根谭

山林是胜地，一营恋便成市朝；书画是雅事，一贪痴便成商贾。盖心无染著，欲境是仙都；心有系恋，乐境成苦海矣。

人生的滋味——菜根谭

芦花被下，卧雪眠云，保全得一窝夜气；竹叶杯中，吟风弄月，躲离了万丈红尘。

Sleeping and playing in nature Escaping the dusty world

1 Reclining beneath a cover of reed flowers, with a bed of snow and a canopy of clouds...

2 Preserves in one a store of refreshing air.

3 Bamboo leaves in a cup of wine, frolicking in natural scenery,

4 Releases one from layers of worldly dust.

Things of nature exude boundless vitality.Coming into contact with nature can renew the spirit.

A world among clouds
A universe in tranquillity

1 Beneath a bamboo fence, I heard the barking of dogs and cackling of chickens and suddenly seemed to be in a world among clouds.

whirr

Inside a window of fragrant rue, I heard the chirring of cicadas and the cawing of crows and came to realize a universe within tranquillity.

When the external world calls after the self has dissolved, both internal and external worlds come sharply into focus.

2

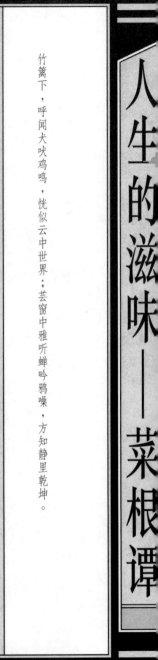

竹篱下，呼闻犬吠鸡鸣，恍似云中世界；芸窗中雅听蝉吟鸦噪，方知静里乾坤。

人生的滋味——菜根谭

我不希荣，何忧乎利禄之香饵？我不竞进，何畏乎仕宦之危机？

I do not hope for splendor,

1

2

So why worry of the bait of emolument and status?

I do not contend for advancement, so why fear the pitfalls of officialdom?

If you can maintain the purity of the original mind, you won't have to worry about being seduced by material things.

3

An inspirational environment Attuning the mind, cultivating the spirit

1

Wandering among mountains, springs, and rocks, my worldly mind gradually ceases to be.

2

Lingering in poetry, calligraphy, and paintings, my vulgar side slowly dissolves.

3

So although a gentleman does not damage his character through material amusements,

4

Yet he uses his environment to reattune his mind.

The beauty of nature cleanses the spirit; poetry, calligraphy, and paintings expand our horizons and elevate our character.

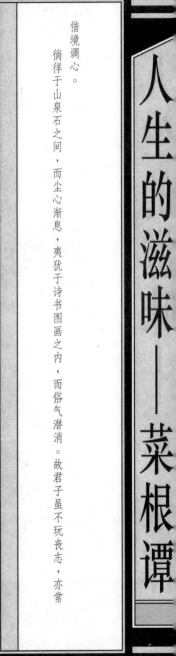

人生的滋味——菜根谭

借境调心。

徜徉于山泉石之间，而尘心渐息，夷犹于诗书图画之内，而俗气潜消。故君子虽不玩丧志，亦常

93

清也。

春日气象繁华，令人心神骀荡，不若秋日云白风清，兰芳桂馥，水天一色，上下空明，使人神骨俱

Better the brisk air of autumn than the vibrancy of spring

1 The scene on a spring day is vibrant and thriving, opening the mind and freeing the spirit.

2 But how much better the crisp breeze and white clouds of an autumn day infused with the fragrance of orchids and sweet osmanthus;

3 The sky and water coalesce, all is clear and bright, purifying both body and spirit.

The spring is vibrant, but how much better the briskness of autumn. In youth, we struggle in the fight for material things, but how much better the refinement and simplicity of old age.

94

Achieve the true sentiments of a poet Realize the mysterious truths of Zen

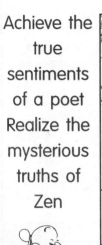

To be illiterate and yet possess the spirit of poetry is to have achieved the true sentiments of a poet;

You should hear the frogs on a spring night beneath the moon!

To have never studied a verse and yet possess the spirit of Zen is to have realized the mysterious truths of Zen.

You turn people into Buddhas, and I turn rocks into Buddhas!

Learning to read and studying the scriptures are helpful in writing poetry and understanding Zen, but they don't make much difference if you don't possess a poet's sentiments or the spirit of Zen.

人生的滋味——菜根谭

一字不识，而有诗意者，得诗家真趣；一偈不参，而有禅味者，悟禅教玄机。

人生的滋味——菜根谭

机动的，弓影疑为蛇蝎，寝石视为伏虎，此中浑是杀气：念息的，石虎可作海鸥，蛙声可当鼓吹，触处俱见真机。

Coming and going at will Dissolved in confident ease

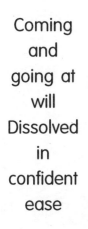

1

The body is like an unmoored boat, drifting or stopping with the current;

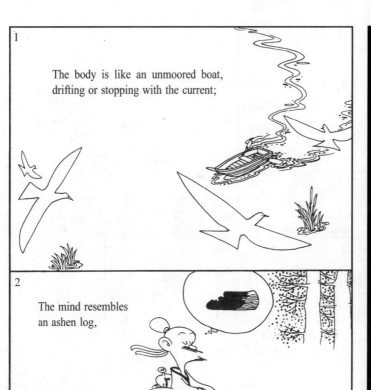

2

The mind resembles an ashen log,

3

Caring not of injury or ornament.

That guy's nothing!

I hate him!

He's so great!

I really like him!

"Don't rejoice over things; don't feel sorry for yourself." If we don't let any external circumstances affect our inner balance, then we can come and go at will and be happy with the world.

人生的滋味——菜根谭

身如不系之舟，一任流行坎止；心似既灰之木，何妨刀割香涂。

人生的滋味——菜根谭

欲其中者，波沸寒潭，山林不见其寂；虚其中者，凉生酷暑，朝市不知其喧。

人生的滋味——菜根谭

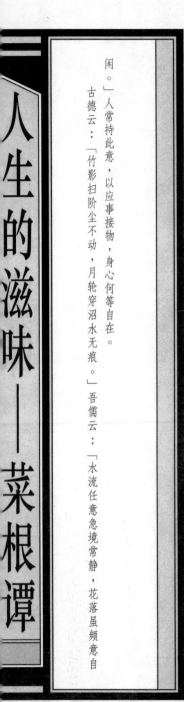

闲。」人常持此意，以应事接物，身心何等自在。

古德云：「竹影扫阶尘不动，月轮穿沼水无痕。」吾儒云：「水流任意急境常静，花落虽频意自

Live life like flowing water, drooping flowers
The body and mind must always be at ease

1 A virtuous monk of old once said, "Bamboo shadows sweep across the steps, but the dust doesn't move."

2 "The lunar orb penetrates a pond, but the water shows no trace."

One of our Confucians said, "Flowing water rushes along, but the surroundings remain still;"

4 "Flowers droop and the petals flutter, but my thoughts are all at ease."

5 If a person can maintain this frame of mind in dealing with the world and handling affairs, how carefree life will be!

We should change with circumstances but not be at the mercy of our surroundings, only in this way can we preserve our original natures.

Living in the world, forget the world
Transcending things, enjoy nature

1

Fish swim around comfortably, forgetting each other in the water.

2

Birds soar on breezes, but don't realize there is wind.

3

If we can understand this, we can transcend the ties of the material world...

4

And enjoy the workings of nature.

A fish swims about so leisurely in the water because it doesn't realize it is even in water. But people get so caught up in material desires that they end up shackled by their own environment.

人生的滋味—菜根谭

鱼得水逝，而相忘乎水；鸟乘风飞，而不知有风。识此可以超物累，可以乐天机。

101

人生的滋味——菜根谭

宠辱不惊，闲看庭前花开花落；去留无意，漫随天外云卷云舒。

Scorn or favor brings no surprise Going or staying makes no difference

You're wonderful!

Is that right?

Is that right?

2

You're despicable!

3

! Favor or scorn brings no surprise, leisurely watching the flowers blossom and fade before the court.

Congratulations, you've been promoted!

Really?

5

You're fired!

Really?

4

6

Going or staying makes no difference, peacefully watching the clouds curl and unfold in the sky.

Don't let being honored or disdained affect your mood. Positions come and go like floating clouds and aren't worth dwelling on.

人生的滋味——菜根谭

不为飞蛾鸱鹦者，几何人哉？

晴空朗月，何处不可翱翔，而飞蛾独投夜烛；清泉绿草，何物不可饮啄，而鸱鹦偏嗜腐鼠。噫！世之

The sea of suffering is vast and far Turn your head to the other shore

1 A clear sky and a bright moon, what place can't you soar to?

2 Yet moths dive into a flame.

3 A clear spring and green herbs, what can't you eat or drink?

4 Yet crows prefer putrid rats...

Alas! How many in the world do not become moths or crows?

5 With the world so vast, you can soar off to anywhere at all, yet most people lock themselves in a tiny little space, blindly pursuing wealth and status just like the moth attracted to a flame.

Seeking the Buddha on the inside Spurning the dharmas on the outside

1

One who sits on a raft then contemplates leaving it is an unattached man of the Dao.

2

One who rides a mule then goes seeking a mule will never be a master of Zen.

A raft is simply a tool to get you to your destination. After getting the fish, forget the net; after getting the rabbit, forget the snare; after getting the meaning, forget the words. The truth is right in front of you, so there's no need to go off in search of it.

才就筏便思舍筏，方是无事道人；若骑驴又复觅驴，终为不了禅师。

人生的滋味——菜根谭

人生的滋味——菜根谭

诗思在灞陵桥上，微吟就，林岫便已浩然；野兴在镜湖曲边，独往时，山川自相映发。

In the charm of the wilds and places replete Poetical springs well up from inside

Poetic thoughts on Ba river bridge,

Softly voicing lines, woods and summits expand before me.

Charm of the wilds at a Jing lake bend,

Roaming all alone, the hills and rivers reflect back and forth.

Open you heart and let nature in, because only someone with an open heart can appreciate the mountains, waters, flowers, and moon.

真空不空，执相非真，破相亦非真，问世尊如何发付？

人生的滋味——菜根谭

在世出世，循欲是苦，绝欲亦是苦，听吾侪善自修持。

5 Ask Sakyamuni for his opinion:

6 "Live in the world, but transcend it."

7 Following desires is suffering;

8 Severing desires is also suffering.

9 Do what we do: rely on your own understanding and ability.

Both living in illusions and emphasizing the unreality of illusions are contrary to the truth. To simultaneously live in the world and transcend it is the best way to get along.

人生的滋味——菜根谭

性天澄徹，即飢餐渴飲，無非康濟身心；心地沉迷，縱談禪演偈，總是播弄精魂。

The genuine
leaves not
the illusory
The refined
leaves not
the
mundane

1

Gold comes from mines, and jade is found in rock;

2

One can only seek the genuine in the illusory.

The Dao is found in wine,

3

And gods are met in flowers; the refined cannot be separated from the mundane.

4

Forsaking the mundane world and living an eccentric life on the edges of society, it's difficult to avoid falling right back into the mundane. If, however, you choose to place yourself in the mundane world, you can rise above the mundane.

111

人生的滋味——菜根谭

神酣布被窝中，得天地冲和之气；味足藜羹饭后，识人生淡泊之真。

A blanket of straw and vegetables plain nourish a natural harmony

1 To slumber deeply under a blanket of coarse cloth...

2 Is to know the harmony of heaven and earth.

3 To relish the taste of rice and pigweed soup...

Is to know the genuineness of a simple life.

4 If you can reduce material needs to their lowest level, you can achieve the greatest heights of spiritual happiness, because then no one can make you do what you don't want to do.

To cut off all your worries
A sunny breeze, an after-rain moon

1
Inside a tiny hut,
a thousand worries are gone;

2
Who cares about painted mansions as high as the clouds or beaded curtains as perfect as raindrops?

3
After three cups, the truth complete has come;

4
All I know are a plain zither playing to the moon...

5
And a short flute singing to the breeze.

If we can get rid of all our worries, we'll be able to experience and enjoy life to the fullest.

斗室中，万虑都捐，说甚画栋飞云，珠帘卷雨；三杯后，一真自得，唯知素琴横月，短笛吟风。

人生的滋味——菜根谭

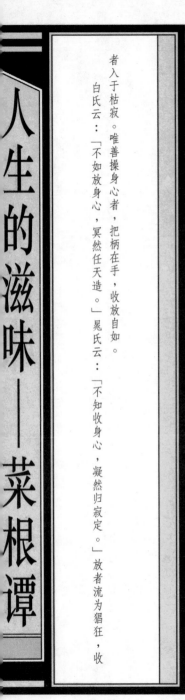

白氏云：「不如放身心，冥然任天造。」晁氏云：「不知收身心，凝然归寂定。」放者流为猖狂，收者入于枯寂。唯善操身心者，把柄在手，收放自如。

Minding the body and mind Freedom in indulgence and restraint

It's best to release the mind and body and blindly follow creation.

Bai Juyi once said:

It's best to restrain the mind and body and wholly return to tranquillity.

Chao Buzhi said:

1

2

An indulgent person can slide into recklessness;

3

A restrained person can lapse into boorishnes.

4

Overindulgence and too much restraint are both extreme behavior. Only by walking the middle path and not straying to either extreme can you transcend the ordinary and enter sageliness.

Only the person who can manage his body and mind well can be as indulgent or tranquil as he pleases.

5

114

Nature and the mind Harmonize as one

On seeing a snowy night...

Or the moon in the sky, one's mood seems purified.

On feeling a springtime wind or warm air, one's thoughts seem harmonized.

Nature and the mind are originally one body; the environment changes with the turnings of the mind, and the mind changes with the transformations of things. By eliminating material desires, we can get at the charm of nature.

Creation and the mind interfuse with no space in between.

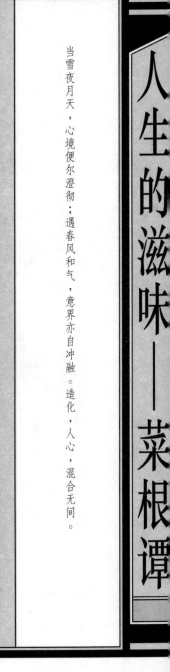

当雪夜月天，心境便尔澄彻；遇春风和气，意界亦自冲融。造化，人心，混合无间。

人生的滋味——菜根谭

115

人生的滋味——菜根谭

尽子收，雌雄安在。

优人傅粉调朱，效妍丑于毫端，俄而歌残场罢，妍丑何存？奕者争先竞后，较雌雄于著子，俄而局

Winner and loser, beautiful and ugly are just momentary illusions

1 The players apply mascara and rouge, becoming pretty or ugly at the tip of a brush.

2 Finally the songs end and the crowds disperse; where are the pretty and ugly now?

3 The competitors vie for first and last, becoming winner or loser as the pieces fall,

Check-mate!

Darn!

4 Finally the games end and the pieces are collected; where are the winner and loser now?

On stage, they are proud and elegant, but behind the curtain they are just actors trying to make a living. At the game board he beats all comers, but when the games are over, he still has to face the mundane world.

116

Good and bad fortune, suffering and joy There is only the difference of a single thought

1 All good and bad fortune in life are created by the mind.

A single thought of purity, and the searing flames become a pond; a single thought of realization, and the boat ascends the Other Shore.

2 If desire for profit is too intense, it becomes a fiery pit; if greedy attachment is too strong, it becomes a sea of suffering.

Therefore, Sakyamuni said:

3 If one's thoughts change slightly, one's realm changes drastically. So can one not be but cautious?!

If the mind is mired in acquisitiveness, and desires for profit are too strong, it's easy to fall into the depths of vice. If we awaken to the truth in time, we can escape the boundless sea of suffering.

池，一念惊觉船登彼岸。」念头稍异，境界顿殊，可不慎哉！

人生福境祸区，皆念想造成。故释氏云：「利欲炽然即是火坑，贪爱沉溺便为苦海；一念清净烈焰成

117

人生的滋味——菜根谭

绳锯木断，水滴石穿，学道者须加力索；水到渠成，瓜熟蒂落，得道者一任天机。

With quiet patience and constant discipline
A foot of iron is ground into a pin

1 A rope saw severs a log;

2 Drops of water penetrate rock a person studying the Dao must be persevering.

3 Water flows into existing channels; melons ripen then drop from the vine.

4 One who has attained the Dao follows the natural processes.

Pursuing enlightenment requires patience and perseverance. After enlightenment, everything comes naturally.

After a rain,
the mountains
seem fresh
In the night, a
bell rings
clear

1

Observing mountain scenery after a rain, the view seems freshly beautiful;

2

Hearing the sound of a bell in the night, the sound seems clear and transcendent.

After a good cleansing in serene surroundings, the mind can naturally manifest its pure and genuine original nature.

雨余观山色，景象便觉新妍；夜静听钟声，音响尤为清越。

人生的滋味——菜根谭

119

人生的滋味——菜根譚

登高使人心旷，临流使人意远；读书于雨雪之夜，使人神清；舒啸于丘阜之巅，使人兴迈。

Snowstorm studying purifies the spirit
Hilltop vistas expand the mind

1 Climbing up high expands the mind;

2 Studying on a snowy night purifies the spirit;

3 Yelling on a hilltop enervates the passions.

4 If you want to open yourself up or cultivate a refined demeanor, the best way is to encounter nature.

Yell

If you want to open yourself up or cultivate a refined demeanor, the best way is to encounter nature.

就一身了一身者，方能以万物付万物；还天下于天下者，方能出世间于世间。

人生的滋味——菜根谭

Understand the self based on the self Allow for things to take care of themselves

1 Only those who understand the self based on the self...

2 Can let the myriad things take care of the myriad things.

3 Only those who return nature to nature...

4 Can transcend the world while in the world.

If you can understand that you are just one small part of the world, you will naturally become fair and unselfish, be able to transcend material objects, and not be shackled by narrow minds.

123

人生的滋味——菜根谭

耳根似飙谷投响，过而不留，则是非俱谢；心境如月池浸色，空而不着，则物我两忘。

A passing wind, the moon's reflection Leave and then are gone

If one's ears resemble the whistling sound of a valley wind that when it leaves is gone...

He is quite good

He's a lout.

He's terrible.

2

Then right and wrong will go as well.

3

If one's mood resembles the floating sight of a moonlit pond, still and undisturbed,

4

Then self and other will be forgotten.

If you can pay no heed to praise and blame, you can maintain purity of mind.Our normal frame of mind should be like water reflecting the moon: still and undisturbed.If we can do this, our troubles and worries will disappear.

On reaching fullness, the moon wanes One who reaches fulfillment abstains

1 To view flowers just blossoming, to drink until slightly tipsy;

2 In the midst of these is wonderful delight.

3 But if continued to the point of dazzling flamboyance or delirious intoxication,

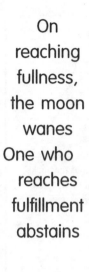

4 It all becomes a vulgar scene.

5 One who has reached the point of fulfillment should consider this.

Only by doing and having just enough can you enjoy the charms of life. Do not upset the balance of life by striving for more than enough.

花看半开，酒饮微醉，此中大有佳趣。若至烂漫酕醄，便成恶境矣。履盈满者，宜思之。

人生的滋味——菜根谭

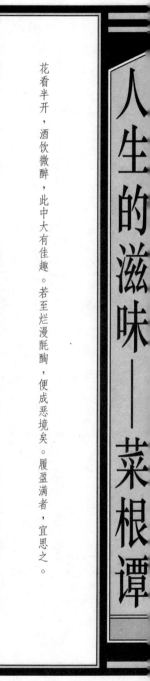

125

人生的滋味——菜根谭

此场中矣。

人生原是一傀儡，只要根蒂在手，一线不乱，卷舒自由，行止在我，一毫不受他人提掇，便超出

Grasp the essentials and move about freely

1 Life is like a marionette,

2 But as long as you hold the sticks, and the strings remain untangled, you can move around as you please.

And with no one to interfere, you can freely leave the stage.

One foot in front of the other!

3

Bye bye!

I can't control myself...

If you can grasp your own nature and not be influenced by your surroundings or other people, you can come and go as you please.

126

Transcend sensual desires Achieve life's delights

1

I don't expect the best tea, yet my pot is never dry;

2

I don't expect strong drink, yet my cup is never empty;

3

My plain zither lacks a string, but still it reattunes me;

4

My short flute lacks a hole, but still it comforts me.

5 6

Although it's difficult to out-do the ancient sage Fu Xi in purity and non-action,

Yet I can match the worthies Ji Kang and Ruan Ji in their casual elegance.

In all affairs, it's enough to find a little enjoyment for yourself. There's no need to be a connoisseur of everything and emphasize outward appearances. Just enjoy simple pleasures and take comfort in your surroundings.

人生的滋味——菜根谭

茶不求精而壶亦不燥，酒不求冽而樽亦不空，素琴无弦而常调，短笛无腔而自适。纵难超越义皇，亦可匹俦嵇阮。

图字：01－2005－5957

图书在版编目(CIP)数据

菜根谭：人生的滋味＝The Roots of Wisdom：The Flavor of Life/蔡志忠绘 . 一北京：现代出版社,2005
(蔡志忠漫画系列)
ISBN 7-80188-656-9

Ⅰ. 菜… Ⅱ. 蔡… Ⅲ. 漫画-作品集-中国-现代 Ⅳ.J228.2

中国版本图书馆 CIP 数据核字(2005)第 136237 号

The Roots of Wisdom：The Flavor of Life
菜根谭：人生的滋味

作者/〔台湾〕蔡志忠
译者/〔美〕Brian Bruya
总策划/吴江江
责任编辑/张　璐
封面设计/刘　刚
出版发行/现代出版社(北京安外安华里 504 号　邮编：100011)
印刷/北京新华印刷厂
开本/880×1230　1/24　5.75 印张
版次/2006 年 1 月第 1 版
　　　2007 年 1 月第 2 次印刷
印数/8001～13000 册
书号/ISBN 7-80188-656-9
定价/14.00 元